Power Maths

Year 2 Practice Book 2C

What would you like to learn to do better in maths this term? Write it here.

This book belongs to _____ .

My class is _____ .

 Pearson

Contents

We will practise different ways to solve problems!

I cannot wait to have a go at these things!

How to use this book

Do you remember how to use this Practice Book?

Use the Textbook first to learn how to solve this type of problem.

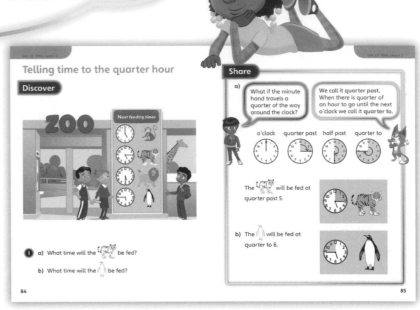

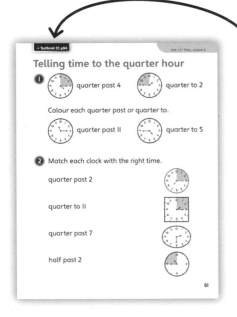

This shows you which Textbook page to use.

Have a go at questions by yourself using this Practice Book. Use what you have learned.

Challenge questions make you think hard!

Questions with this light bulb make you think differently.

Reflect

Each lesson ends with a Reflect question so you can show how much you have learned.

Show what you have done in My Power Points at the back of this book.

Reflect

Which of these clocks shows quarter to 6?

Tell a partner how you know the answer.

My journal

At the end of a unit your teacher will ask you to fill in My journal.

This will help you show how much you can do now that you have finished the unit.

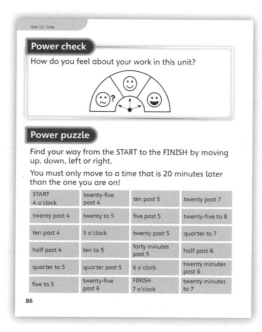

→ Textbook 2C p116   Unit 13: Time

End of unit check

My journal

The answers to these times have been given to you.

Explain how you know whether they are right.

I know the time is twenty-five minutes past 6

because _____

_____

I know the time is twenty minutes to 3

because _____

_____

These words might help you.

hour hand

minute hand

85

Unit 13: Time

Power check

How do you feel about your work in this unit?

Power puzzle

Find your way from the START to the FINISH by moving up, down, left or right.

You must only move to a time that is 20 minutes later than the one you are on!

START 4 o'clock	twenty-five past 4	ten post 5	twenty past 7
twenty past 4	twenty to 5	five past 5	twenty-five to 8
ten past 4	5 o'clock	twenty past 5	quarter to 7
half past 4	ten to 5	forty minutes past 5	half past 6
quarter to 5	quarter past 5	6 o'clock	twenty minutes past 6
five to 5	twenty-five past 6	FINISH 7 o'clock	twenty minutes to 7

86

Describing movement

a) Which person is standing to the left of ⬛³ ?

Person ⬜ is standing to the left of ⬛³ .

b) Which person is standing between ⬛¹ and ⬛³ ?

Person ⬜ is standing between ⬛¹ and ⬛³ .

2 **a)** Which item is above the ☕ ?

The _____ is above

the ☕ .

b) Kim puts a flower below the picture frame.

Draw the flower on a shelf.

Describe the position of the flower in another way.

_____

_____

3 Complete the sentences.

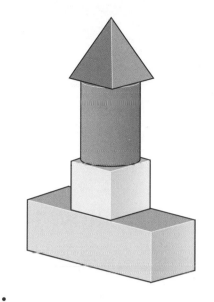

   a) The cube is between the

     _____ and _____ .

   b) The cylinder is on top of the

     _____ and the _____ .

4 Start at the shaded square.

Follow the instructions in each square you land on.

Number the squares in the correct order.

I down, 2 right	2 down, I right	2 left, I down
I right, I up	I right, I up	I down, 2 left
I up, I right	2 up, I left	I left

7

5

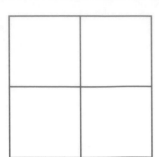

CHALLENGE

Follow the instructions to complete the grid.

a) The circle is above the square.

b) The square is to the right of the triangle.

c) The rectangle is to the left of the circle.

Reflect

Here is a grid.

Describe the position of the star to a partner.

Is there another way to describe the position of the star?

I could say _____

_____

_____ .

Describing turns

1 Circle the correct word in each sentence.

a)

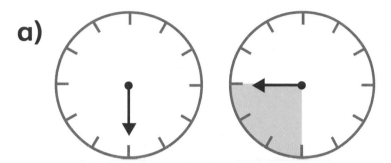

The arrow moved a quarter turn
clockwise / anticlockwise.

b)

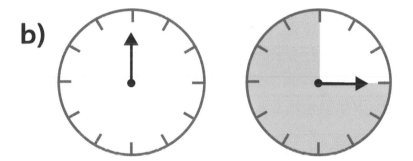

The arrow moved a three-quarter turn
clockwise / anticlockwise.

c)

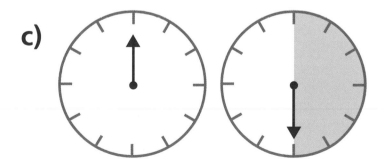

The arrow moved a half turn
clockwise / anticlockwise.

2 Complete the sentences to describe the turns.

a)

The ladybird moved a _____
turn clockwise.

b)

The ladybird moved a _____
turn anticlockwise.

c)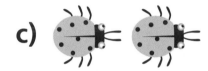

The ladybird moved a _____
turn clockwise.

3 Match each image to the correct description.

Quarter turn clockwise

Whole turn anticlockwise

Half turn clockwise

4 Here is a fly. It has turned clockwise.

Do you agree?

I wonder if it is always quicker to turn clockwise.

Circle your answer and explain.   Yes / No

_____

_____

Reflect

Here is a house.

Draw the turns in the boxes below.

Half turn clockwise	Three-quarter turn anticlockwise	Quarter turn clockwise

→ Textbook 2C p16

Describing movement and turns

1 The pirate moves to the treasure.
Put an X where the treasure is.
Instructions to find the treasure:

Forwards 2

Quarter turn clockwise

Forwards 1

2 Complete the sentences to get the to the  .

clockwise
anticlockwise
forwards
backwards
quarter

Go [ ] spaces _____.

Make a _____ turn

_____.

Go [ ] spaces _____.

12

3 Match each image to the correct instructions to get from the Start to the .

a)

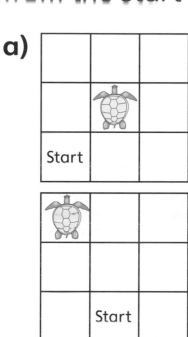

Forwards 2, quarter turn anticlockwise, forwards 1

Forwards 2, quarter turn clockwise, forwards 2

Forwards 1, quarter turn clockwise, forwards 1

b) Create your own instructions for the grid below.

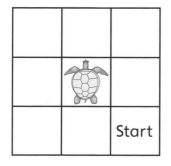

You could start with a turn or you could start by moving forwards.

_____

_____

4 Is Tom correct? How do you know?

A quarter turn clockwise is the same as a three-quarter turn anticlockwise.

I am going to try it for myself.

_____

_____

Reflect

Draw the arrow in a different position.

Can your partner describe how you have turned it?

I will try to describe my partner's arrow in two ways!

Making patterns with shapes

1 Circle the shape that goes in the space in the pattern.

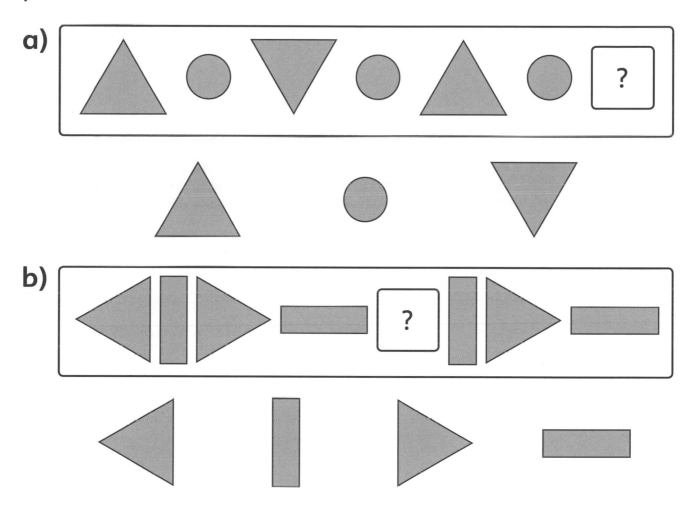

2 Draw the missing shape in each pattern.

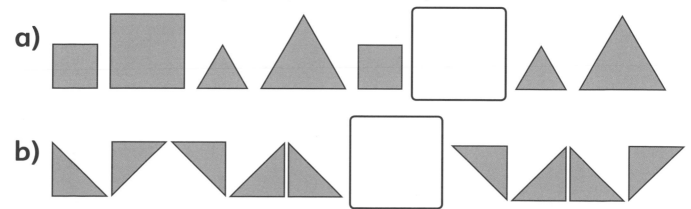

3 Draw the next two shapes in each pattern.

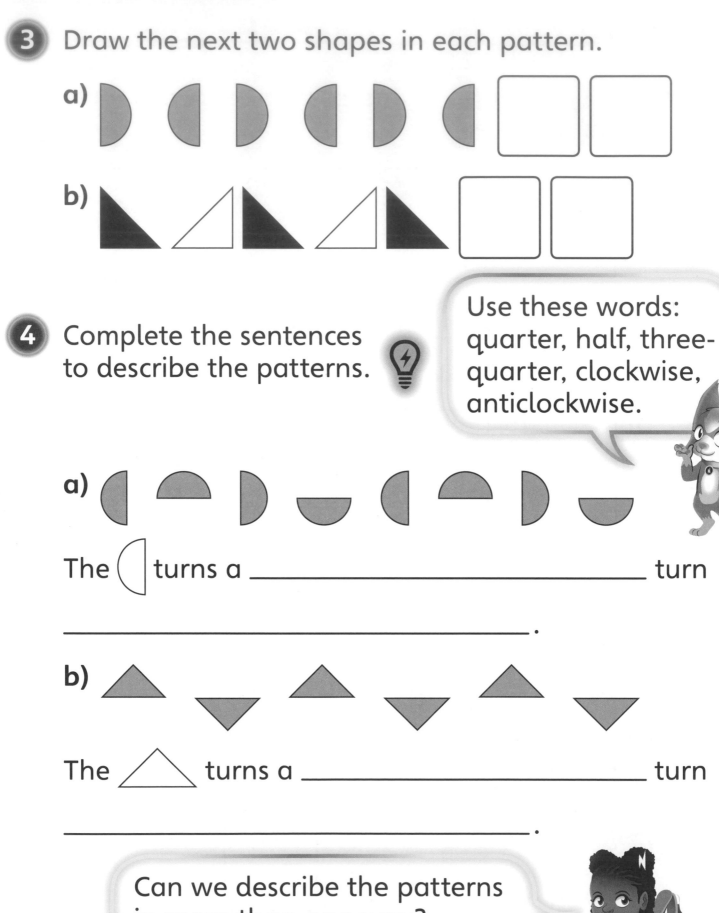

a)

b)

4 Complete the sentences to describe the patterns.

Use these words: quarter, half, three-quarter, clockwise, anticlockwise.

a)

The ◖ turns a _____ turn

_____.

b)

The △ turns a _____ turn

_____.

Can we describe the patterns in more than one way?

5 Circle the odd one out.

CHALLENGE

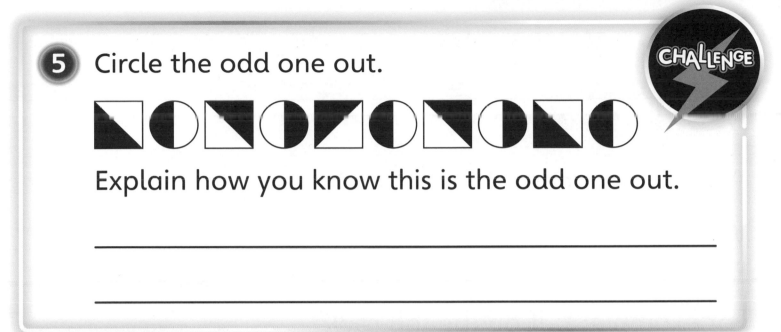

Explain how you know this is the odd one out.

_____

_____

Reflect

Trace around two different shapes.

Make a repeating pattern for your partner to describe.

→ Textbook 2C p24

End of unit check

My journal

Ask your partner to choose an item.

Write out questions you could ask to work out which item they have chosen.

For example: Is it on the top row?

These words might help you.

left   **right**

above   **below**

top   **bottom**

18

Power check

How do you feel about your work in this unit?

Power play

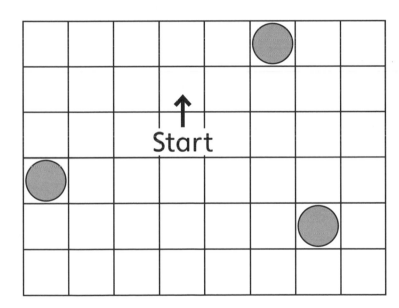

- ▪ = move forwards 1
- ▪ = move forwards 2
- ▪ = move backwards 1
- ▪ = move backwards 2
- ▪ = quarter turn clockwise
- ▪ = quarter turn anticlockwise

- Begin at the Start square and roll a dice to find how you must move.

- Take it in turns to roll the dice.

- The first person to land on a grey circle wins.

- If you cannot finish a move, you must miss a turn.

My way, your way!

1 There are 55 children on a school trip.

There are 27 boys. How many children are girls?

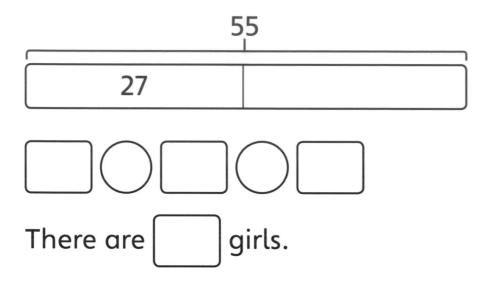

There are ☐ girls.

2 A shopkeeper sells 19 apples on Saturday. He sells 49 apples on Sunday.

How many apples does he sell in total?

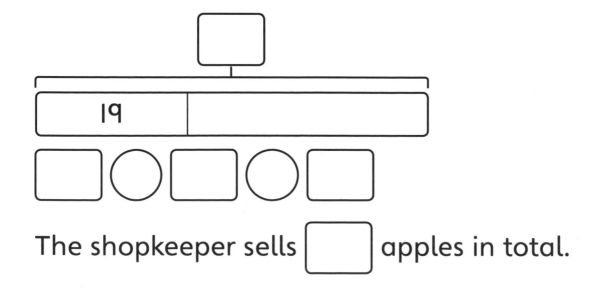

The shopkeeper sells ☐ apples in total.

3 Stacey is 37. Her mum is 78.

How many years older is Stacey's mum than Stacey?

Stacey

Stacey's mum

Stacey's mum is ☐ years older than Stacey.

4 Mo is watching cartoons.

'Dreams' cartoon is 32 minutes long.

'Starry Night' cartoon is 12 minutes shorter.

How many minutes long is 'Starry Night'?

Dreams

Starry Night

12

'Starry Night' is ☐ minutes long.

⑤

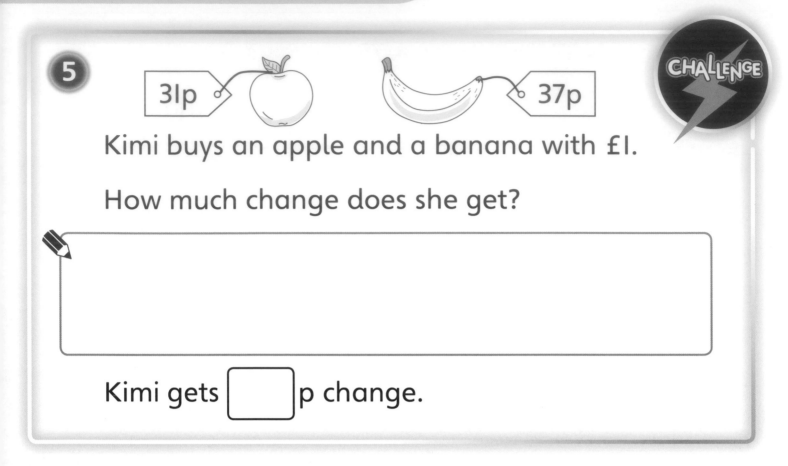

31p

37p

Kimi buys an apple and a banana with £1.

How much change does she get?

Kimi gets ☐ p change.

CHALLENGE

Reflect

Oskar has £40. He is given another £35.

How much does he have in total?

I wonder what methods my friends used.

Oskar has £ ☐ in total.

Using number facts

1 **a)** 37 + 6 = 43

Use this calculation to help you complete these questions.

47 + 6 = ☐   57 + 6 = ☐

6 + 67 = ☐   ☐ + 6 = 33

b) 63 + 8 = 71

Use this calculation to help you complete these questions.

83 + 8 = ☐   8 + 33 = ☐

28 + 43 = ☐   ☐ + 58 = 71

2 Match the calculations that have the same answer.

30 + 5   60 + 35

50 + 5   30 + 25

60 + 5   20 + 15

90 + 5   50 + 15

3 Use the answer from scale A to work out the total weight for scale B.

33g + 45g   15g + 33g

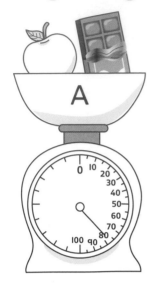 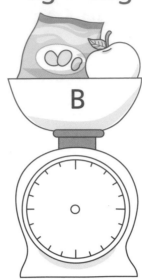

The total weight for scale B is ☐.

4 Look at this calculation: 75 + 8 = 83.

Now solve each calculation and match it to the words that describe it.

75 + 7   one more

65 + 8   one less

75 + 18   10 more

65 + 19   equal to

45 + 38   10 less

24

5 Casey has two boxes of cakes.

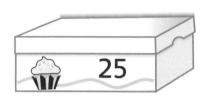 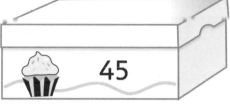 = 70

Nadia has two boxes of cakes.

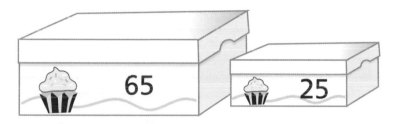

How many more cakes does Nadia have than Casey?

I wonder if we can work this out without a written calculation?

Nadia has ⬜ more cakes than Casey.

Reflect

What is the difference between the missing numbers? Explain how you know.

$45 + \boxed{} = 60$ $45 + \boxed{} = 80$

→ Textbook 2C p36

Using number facts and equivalence

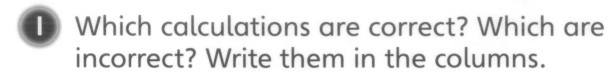

1 Which calculations are correct? Which are incorrect? Write them in the columns.

$32 + 30 = 62$

$2 + 45 = 65$

$17 + 53 = 60$

$75 - 15 = 90$

$58 - 20 - 10 - 10 - 10 = 8$

$40 - 40 = 40$

Correct	Incorrect

2 Find the mistake. Write the calculation correctly.

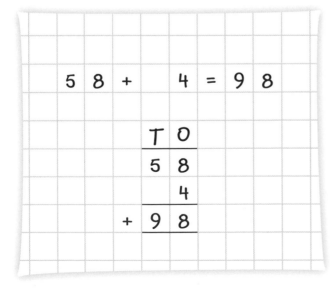

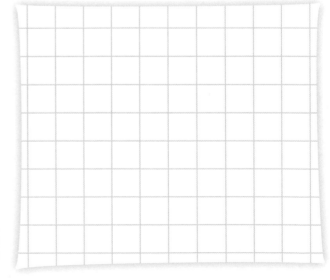

3 Sol works out 100 – 76 using the column method.

T	O
$\cancel{1}$ $\cancel{\overset{9}{10}}$	$\overset{1}{0}$
– 7	6
2	4

a) Is this the most efficient way? Circle Yes or No, then explain why.

Yes / No

_____

_____

_____

b) Work this out in another way.

27

④ Look at Sofia's calculation.

$45 + 29 = \boxed{}$

$45 + 30 = 75 + 1 = 76$

$45 + 29 = 76$

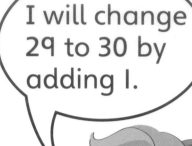

I will change 29 to 30 by adding 1.

Explain Sofia's mistake.

_____

_____

Reflect

$47 + 13 = \boxed{}$

Is the correct answer 50, 60 or 34? Explain why someone might find the two incorrect answers.

_____

_____

_____

Using a 100 square

1

1	2	3	4	5	6	7	8	9	10
11	12	13	14	15	16	17	18	19	20
21	22	23	24	25	26	27	28	29	30
31	32	33	34	35	36	37	38	39	40
41	42	43	44	45	46	47	48	49	50
51	52	53	54	55	56	57	58	59	60
61	62	63	64	65	66	67	68	69	70
71	72	73	74	75	76	77	78	79	80
81	82	83	84	85	86	87	88	89	90
91	92	93	94	95	96	97	98	99	100

Use the 100 square to answer these calculations.

a) $54 + 5 =$

b) $44 - 8 =$

c) $73 + 9 =$

d) $34 - 20 =$

2 Use the 100 square to answer these calculations.

a) $33 + 16 =$

b) $26 + 38 =$

c) $87 - 67 =$

d) $88 - 78 =$

3 Use the 100 square to complete these calculations.

a) $36 + \boxed{} = 79$

b) $52 - \boxed{} = 23$

c) $97 - 17 =$

d) $\boxed{} = 38 + 19$

29

4 Frank works out 27 + 38 on a 100 square.

1	2	3	4	5	6	7	8	9	10
11	12	13	14	15	16	17	18	19	20
21	22	23	24	25	26	27	28	29	30
31	32	33	34	35	36	37	38	39	40
41	42	43	44	45	46	47	48	49	50
51	52	53	54	55	56	57	58	59	60
61	62	63	64	65	66	67	68	69	70
71	72	73	74	75	76	77	78	79	80
81	82	83	84	85	86	87	88	89	90
91	92	93	94	95	96	97	98	99	100

> I counted on in 10s, then I counted on in 1s.

a) Show this on a number line.

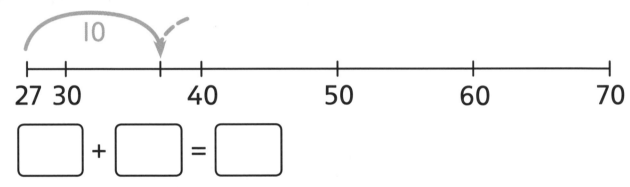

[ ] + [ ] = [ ]

b) Show 52 – 14 on a 100 square and a number line.

1	2	3	4	5	6	7	8	9	10
11	12	13	14	15	16	17	18	19	20
21	22	23	24	25	26	27	28	29	30
31	32	33	34	35	36	37	38	39	40
41	42	43	44	45	46	47	48	49	50
51	52	53	54	55	56	57	58	59	60
61	62	63	64	65	66	67	68	69	70
71	72	73	74	75	76	77	78	79	80
81	82	83	84	85	86	87	88	89	90
91	92	93	94	95	96	97	98	99	100

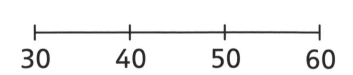

[ ] – [ ] = [ ]

5 Some numbers have been shaded on the 100 square.

1	2	3	4	5	6	7	8	9	10
11	12	13	14	15	16	17	18	19	20
21	22	23	24	25	26	27	28	29	30
31	32	33	34	35	36	37	38	39	40
41	42	43	44	45	46	47	48	49	50
51	52	53	54	55	56	57	58	59	60
61	62	63	64	65	66	67	68	69	70
71	72	73	74	75	76	77	78	79	80
81	82	83	84	85	86	87	88	89	90
91	92	93	94	95	96	97	98	99	100

What do you notice about the 1s and the 10s?

_____

_____

Reflect

$12 + 43 = $ ☐

Use the 100 square to work this out, starting at 12.

Then swap the numbers and work it out again, this time starting at 43.

1	2	3	4	5	6	7	8	9	10
11	12	13	14	15	16	17	18	19	20
21	22	23	24	25	26	27	28	29	30
31	32	33	34	35	36	37	38	39	40
41	42	43	44	45	46	47	48	49	50
51	52	53	54	55	56	57	58	59	60
61	62	63	64	65	66	67	68	69	70
71	72	73	74	75	76	77	78	79	80
81	82	83	84	85	86	87	88	89	90
91	92	93	94	95	96	97	98	99	100

Discuss with a partner what you noticed about the answers.

→ Textbook 2C p44

Getting started

1 Use the number cards to complete the number sentences.

$$\boxed{} + \boxed{} = 11$$

$$\boxed{} - \boxed{} = 1$$

| 7 | 2 | 6 | 9 |

2 Complete the following number sentences in different ways.

$$\boxed{} + \boxed{} = 16 \qquad\qquad \boxed{} + \boxed{} = 16$$

$$\boxed{} + \boxed{} + \boxed{} = 16 \qquad \boxed{} + \boxed{} + \boxed{} = 16$$

3

| 9 | 6 | 8 | 3 |

a) What is the smallest 2-digit number you can make using two of these cards? $\boxed{}$

b) What is the greatest 2-digit number you can make using two of these cards? $\boxed{}$

How do you know?

4 The prices of sweets are:

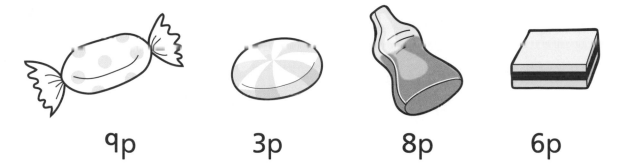

9p   3p   8p   6p

a) How much does this bag of sweets cost?

□ + □ + □ = □

The bag of sweets costs □ p.

b) Can you make a bag of three sweets that costs 23p?

□ + □ + □ = 23p

c) Can you make a bag of four sweets that costs 23p? (You can use each sweet more than once.)

□ + □ + □ + □ = 23p

⑤ Complete these calculations.

CHALLENGE

I think there might be more than one way to do this.

$$4\boxed{} + \boxed{} = 56$$

$$65 = \boxed{}8 + \boxed{}$$

Reflect

What numbers could go in the boxes?

3	5	8
2	4	6

5   9

		10
		12

8   ?

Share your answers with a partner and discuss what you each did.

Missing numbers

1 **a)** Complete the fact family shown in the part-whole model.

☐ + ☐ = ☐

☐ + ☐ = ☐

☐ − ☐ = ☐

☐ − ☐ = ☐

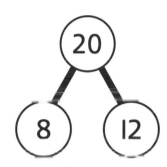

b) Use the number cards to create a fact family.

☐ + ☐ = ☐

☐ + ☐ = ☐

☐ − ☐ = ☐

☐ − ☐ = ☐

| 51 | 35 | 16 |

2 Write a calculation to find the missing part, like this.

$35 - 10 =$

a)  =

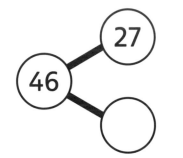

b)  =

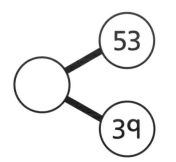

3 Work out the missing numbers.

a) ☐ $+ 14 = 35$

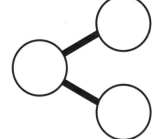

c) $58 -$ ☐ $= 24$

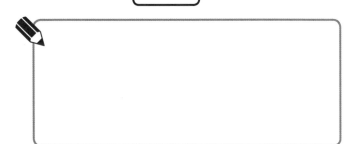

b) $30 +$ ☐ $= 55$

d) ☐ $- 42 = 26$

4 Find three different ways to complete this missing number problem.

$\boxed{}$ + 23 = $\boxed{}$ 4

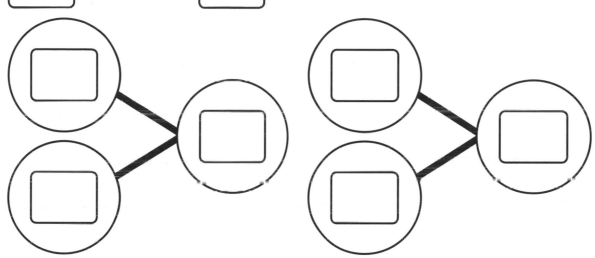

Reflect

Choose a calculation to work out.

$\boxed{}$ + 18 = 50

$\boxed{}$ − 62 = 37

24 + $\boxed{}$ = 74

81 − $\boxed{}$ = 46

Explain how you solved it.

→ Textbook 2C p52

Mental addition and subtraction ❶

1 Work these calculations out mentally.

a) 12 + 5 = ☐   2 + 5 = 7

22 + 5 = ☐   2 + 5 = 7

32 + 5 = ☐   52 + 5 = ☐

☐2 + 5 = 9☐   ☐ + 5 = 77

b) 17 − 4 = 13   27 − 4 = ☐

37 − 4 = ☐   57 − ☐ = 53

☐7 − ☐ = 83

2 Put a cross by the calculations that must be wrong.

45 + 3 = 47   ▩2 + 4 = 38   26 + 2 = 29

64 − 3 = 62   ▩8 − 5 = 93

3 Complete these calculations.

a) $24 + 10 = \boxed{}$ $24 + 20 = \boxed{}$

$24 + 30 = \boxed{}$ $50 + 24 = \boxed{}$

$\boxed{} + 50 = 94$

b) $72 - 10 = \boxed{}$ $72 - 20 = \boxed{}$

$73 - 30 = \boxed{}$ $\boxed{} = 73 - 50$

$23 = 73 - \boxed{}$

4 Use this mental method to solve these calculations.

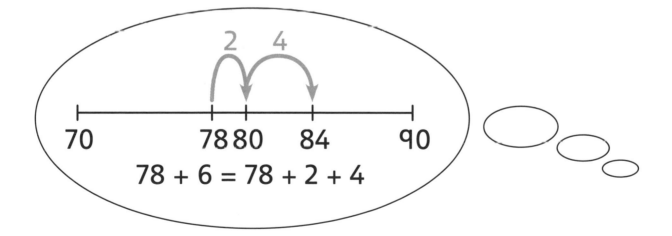

$78 + 6 = 78 + 2 + 4$

a) $78 + 6 = \boxed{}$ c) $53 + 8 = \boxed{}$

b) $7 + 46 = \boxed{}$ d) $28 + 5 = \boxed{}$

39

5

CHALLENGE

Kamran

Poppy

68, 69, 70, 71, 72, 73, 74, 75

Which method would you use to solve 75 – 68?
Explain why.

I would choose Kamran's / Poppy's method because _____

_____

_____

Reflect

Work out one calculation and explain to a friend how you did it.

| 34 + 4 = | 34 + 20 = | 79 – 5 = | 79 – 55 = |

The calculation I chose is _____

My method to work it out was _____

_____

_____

Mental addition and subtraction ❷

1 Complete these calculations.

$26 + 9 = \boxed{}$ $34 - 9 = \boxed{}$

$43 + 8 = \boxed{}$ $26 - 8 = \boxed{}$

$27 + 29 = \boxed{}$ $45 - 28 = \boxed{}$

$68 + 28 = \boxed{}$ $32 - 19 = \boxed{}$

Remember to do these in your head.

2 Complete these calculations.

a) $78 + 18$

To work this out, I can add $\boxed{}$ and then subtract $\boxed{}$.

$78 + 20 - \boxed{} = \boxed{}$

b) $26 + 59$

To work this out, I can add $\boxed{}$ and then subtract $\boxed{}$.

$26 + 60 - \boxed{} = \boxed{}$

3 Samira draws this to help her answer 80 – 45.

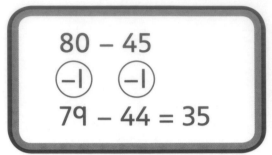

Use it to help you work out these calculations.

a) 70 – 38 = ☐

c) 90 – 49 = ☐

b) 30 – 17 = ☐

d) 100 – 26 = ☐

Explain how you got your answers.

_____

_____

4 Draw lines to match the calculations that give the same answers.

35 + 19   39 – 26

90 – 55   45 + 20

40 – 27   34 + 20

47 + 18   89 – 54

5 ☐ − ☐ = 26

CHALLENGE

To work out this calculation, Dylan subtracted 40 and then added one. The answer was 26.

What calculation did he do?

Reflect

Write a top tip for adding 18.

Write a top tip for subtracting 19.

→ Textbook 2C p60

Efficient subtraction

1 Complete the calculations.

a) 83 – 5 = ☐

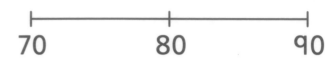

70   80   90

b) 21 – 4 = ☐

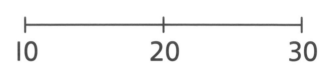

10   20   30

c) 61 – 58 = ☐

Do you do all these in the same way?

2 Work out these calculations.

a) 57 – 16 = ☐

c) 67 – 55 = ☐

b) 98 – 34 = ☐

d) 74 – 74 = ☐

3 **a)** Carlos has 92 stamps. Tilly has 80 fewer stamps.

How many stamps does Tilly have?

Tilly has ☐ stamps.

b) Barney and Marek play a game.

Their total score is 71.

Barney's score is 44. What is Marek's score?

Marek's score is ☐ points.

4 Complete these calculations.

76 − 38 = ☐   76 − 36 = ☐

76 − 37 = ☐   76 − 35 = ☐

What do you notice about the answers?

_____

_____

5 Maryam works out 76 – 68.

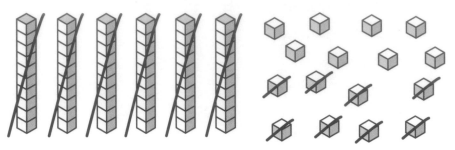

Is this the most efficient way of doing this?

Yes / No

Can you suggest a different method?

_____

_____

Reflect

What is the best subtraction method for these calculations?

82 – 4 = ⬚   82 – 75 = ⬚   82 – 29 = ⬚

_____

_____

Solving problems – addition and subtraction

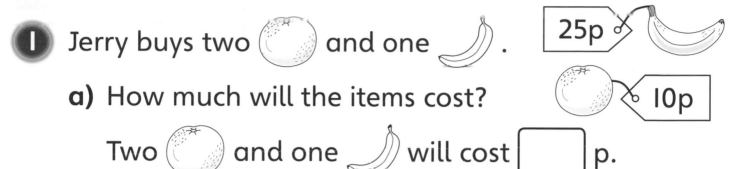

1   Jerry buys two ⬭ and one 🍌.

25p

10p

   a) How much will the items cost?

   Two ⬭ and one 🍌 will cost ⬜ p.

   b) How much change will Jerry get from £1?

   100p − ⬜ = ⬜

   He will get ⬜ p change.

2   Chen has 23 sweets. Annie has 4 more sweets than Chen.

   a) How many sweets does Annie have?

   Annie has ⬜ sweets.

   b) Annie eats 9 sweets.
      How many sweets does Annie now have?

   Annie now has ⬜ sweets.

3 Children in a school were asked about their favourite sports.

Sport	Number of children
football	16
rugby	27
tennis	11
basketball	5

How many more children like rugby more than tennis?

☐ ◯ ☐ = ☐

☐ children like rugby more than tennis.

4

12p

20p

35p

SMILE

I wonder if I can work this out without adding.

Lucy buys a balloon and a party blower.

Cooper buys a balloon and a badge.

Who spends more?

_____ spends more because _____.

5

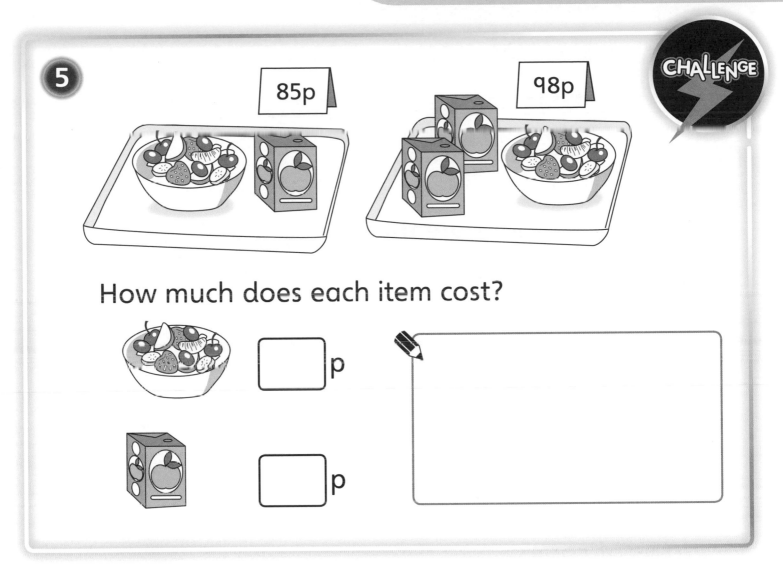

CHALLENGE

How much does each item cost?

p

p

Reflect

Make up a story for one of these calculations.

| 28 + 6 | 28 – 6 |

→ Textbook 2C p68

Solving problems – multiplication and division

1 There are six snails under each stone.

How many snails are there altogether?

There are ⬚ snails altogether.

2 Mr Baker puts out eight rows of chairs.

There are five chairs in each row.

How many chairs are there in total?

There are ⬚ chairs in total.

3 Freddie needs 60 carrots for his horses.

Carrots come in bags of 10.

How many bags does Freddie need?

Freddie needs ☐ bags.

4 Max and Padma share these balloons equally between them.

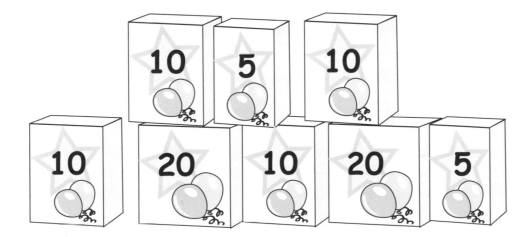

10 5 10

10 20 10 20 5

How many do they each get?

Max and Padma get ☐ balloons each.

51

5 Kofi has six .

Abby has four times as many  as Kofi.

How many  do they have altogether?

CHALLENGE

Kofi and Abby have ☐  altogether.

Reflect

Make a word problem for one of these calculations.

4 × 10 =	40 ÷ 10 =

Solving problems using the four operations

1 Put a different number in each box to make the calculations correct.

$\boxed{}$ + $\boxed{}$ = 20

$\boxed{}$ − $\boxed{}$ = 10

$\boxed{}$ × $\boxed{}$ = 20

$\boxed{}$ ÷ $\boxed{}$ = 10

2 Zac has seven . He spends   .

How much does he have left?

Zac has $\boxed{}$ p left.

53

3 There are 40 sweets altogether.

Three children each take five sweets.

How many sweets are left?

⬛ sweets are left.

4 Tia wants to swim 100 m.

> I length = 10 metres

She swims six lengths.

How many metres does she have left to swim?

Tia has ⬛ m left to swim.

5 Calvin has 30p in altogether.

He has 12  in one hand.

How many are in his other hand?

There are [ ] in his other hand.

Reflect

Step 1: $18 ÷ 2 = 9$

Step 2: $9 - 5 = 4$

Can your partner solve your story?

Write a story problem that needs both steps.

→ Textbook 2C p76

End of unit check

My journal

Explain the steps you need to solve this question.

Oranges are packed into boxes of four.

I have ten boxes of oranges.

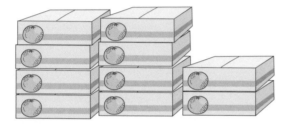

The oranges are put into bags of five.

How many bags of five oranges do I have?

- First I _____
  _____ .
- Then I _____
  _____ .
- I got the answer _____ .

Power check

How do you feel about your work in this unit?

Power play

Hansel and Gretel go into the woods.

Hansel has 26 pieces of bread. Gretel has 24 pieces of bread.

How many pieces of bread do they have in total?

Hansel drops 13 pieces and Gretel drops 7 pieces to the floor.

How many pieces of bread are left in total now?

They meet 5 birds and share the rest of the bread out equally. How many pieces of bread do 3 of the birds get altogether?

→ Textbook 2C p80

Telling and writing time to the hour and the half hour

1 Match each clock with the correct time.

half past 2

half past 1

2 o'clock

9 o'clock

2 What time is it?

 It is _____ past _____ .

 It is _____ .

 It is _____ .

58

3 Draw each time.

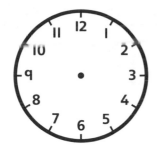 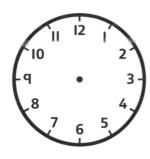 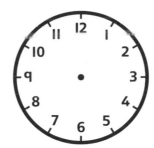 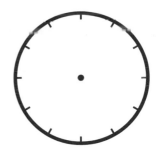

half past II   8 o'clock   half past 6   I o'clock

4 Sam has written these answers.

What mistake is she making each time?

half past 4   II o'clock   half past 7

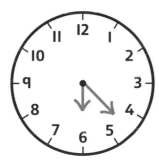      

_____

_____

_____

5 The minute hand is pointing to the 12.

The hour hand is pointing to an odd number.

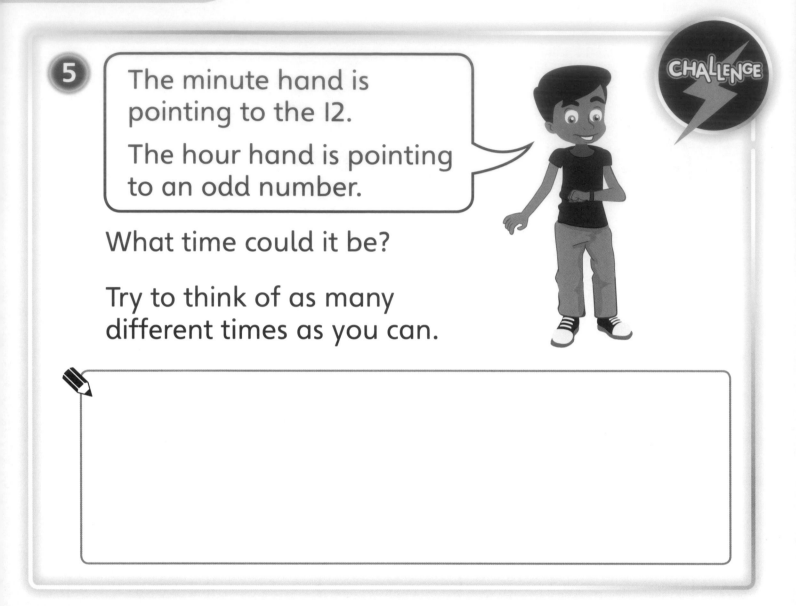

CHALLENGE

What time could it be?

Try to think of as many different times as you can.

Reflect

What is always the same about these times?

- An o'clock time always _____
- _____
- A half past time always _____
- _____
- _____

Telling time to the quarter hour

 1

 quarter past 4

 quarter to 2

Colour each quarter past or quarter to.

 quarter past 11

 quarter to 5

2 Match each clock with the right time.

quarter past 2

quarter to 11

quarter past 7

half past 2

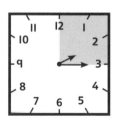

3 What time is it?

a)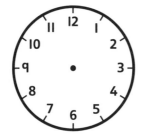

_____

b)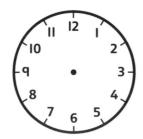

_____

c) The minute hand is pointing to the 9. The hour hand has almost reached the 5.

_____

4 Draw each time on the clocks.

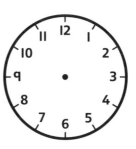

quarter past 6

quarter to 10

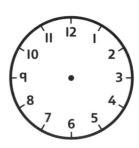

quarter past 8

quarter to 4

5 Malik has tried to make quarter to 2 on this clock.

What mistake has he made?

6 What do the words 'past' and 'to' mean in times?

Half past what?
Quarter to what?

Quarter past a time means _____ .

Half past a time means _____ .

Quarter to a time means _____ .

Reflect

Which of these clocks shows quarter to 6?

Tell a partner how you know the answer.

→ Textbook 2C p88

Telling time to 5 minutes

1 Match the activities with the correct times.

ten to 7   twenty-five   twenty past 3   ten past 5
            past 8

2 Draw the minute hand for each time.

five past 6

twenty-five past 10

ten to 4

twenty-five to 11

3 **a)** Circle the bus that leaves at ten past 12.

b) Circle the bus that leaves at ten to 12.

c) What time does bus C leave?

A   B   C

4 The time is ten minutes to 8.

Which number will the minute hand point to?

How do you know?

5

CHALLENGE

It is thirty-five minutes past 7.

You are both right!

It is twenty-five to 8.

Explain how they can both be right.

I wonder if I can say any other times in two ways.

_____

_____

_____

Reflect

If the time is twenty minutes past, what number will the minute hand point to?

How did you find the answer?

_____

_____

_____

Minutes in an hour

1 I hour and 5 minutes is the same as [ ] minutes.

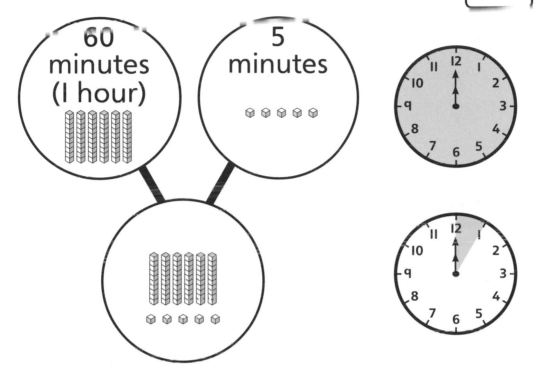

2 Show 85 minutes by colouring the clocks.

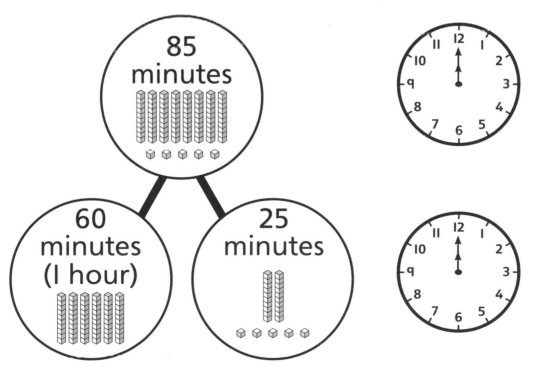

3 **a)** A film lasts for 1 hour and 15 minutes.

Colour in the clocks to show this.

How many minutes does the film last?

The film lasts for [ ] minutes.

b) Another film lasts for 90 minutes.

Colour the clocks to show this.

How many hours and minutes does this film last?

The film lasts for [ ] hour and [ ] minutes.

4 A plane flight takes more than 1 hour, but less than 77 minutes.

How many minutes could the flight take?

CHALLENGE

Reflect

How many minutes are in one hour?

I know! It is 12 because the numbers on a clock go up to 12!

That is not correct. But mistakes are great because we can learn from them!

How do you know the answer?

→ Textbook 2C p96

Finding durations of time

1 Each car starts at a different time.

How much time does each car take?

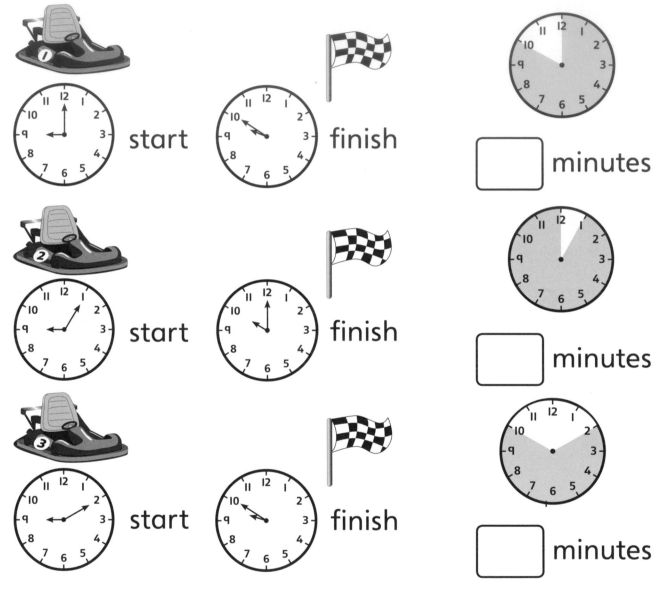

start   finish   ☐ minutes

start   finish   ☐ minutes

start   finish   ☐ minutes

2 How much time has gone by?

☐ minutes have gone by.

3 How much time goes by?

Make ten minutes past 8 on a clock.

Then move the minute hand to show twenty-five minutes to 9.

Think about how many minutes past 8 is the same as twenty-five to 9.

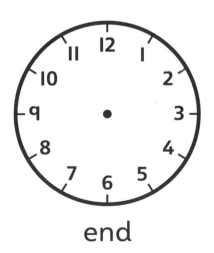

☐ minutes goes by.

4 Class Two's spelling test started at ten minutes past 11. It ended at half past 11.

Draw the start and end times of the test.

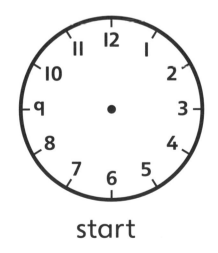

start

end

The spelling test was ☐ minutes long.

5 A television programme lasts 35 minutes.

What times could the programme start and end?

CHALLENGE

I can think of more than one answer!

Reflect

Mum leaves home at five minutes past 8.

She arrives at school at half past 8.

How long did the journey take?

The journey took ☐ minutes

Tell a partner how you found the answer. Did your partner do it the same way as you?

Comparing durations of time

 1

How long is each film?

Lost Island lasts ☐ hours.

Dino Drama lasts ☐ hours.

Which film is longer? _____

2 Which activity is shorter?

School Timetable

Craft Morning:
2 hours and 35 minutes

Sports Afternoon:
2 hours and 10 minutes

☐ hours and ☐ minutes is less than

☐ hours and ☐ minutes.

The _____ is shorter.

3 Mia bakes a chocolate cake from ten past 4 until 5 o'clock.

Hamza bakes a fruit cake from 5 o'clock until twenty to 6.

Whose cake takes longer to bake?

_____ cake takes longer to bake.

How do you know?

_____

_____

4 Compare your times with a partner.

you   your partner

start   finish   start   finish

Count from your start times to your finish times.

Whose time was longer? _____

74

5

Sam: I started my test at half past 2 and stopped at 3 o'clock.

Jane: I started at 2 o'clock, I took more than twice as long!

What times could Jane have ended the test?

Try to think of more than one answer.

Reflect

start   finish   start   finish

To work out which takes longer, I need to

→ Textbook 2C p104

Finding the end time

1 Kat fell asleep at quarter past 3.
She slept for 20 minutes.

What time did she wake up?

start time

time taken

end time

Kat woke up at _____ .

2 Maria and her mum took their dog for a walk
at twenty-five minutes past 6. The walk took 35
minutes.

What time did it end?

Colour the time taken on the second clock. Then
complete the third clock.

start time

time taken

end time

Their walk ended at _____ .

3 A helicopter takes off at twenty minutes past 4. It flies for 20 minutes before it lands.

What time does it land?

      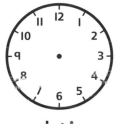

start time   time taken   end time

The helicopter lands at _____ .

4 Molly leaves for school at ten minutes past 8. It takes her 40 minutes.

Kasim leaves for school at twenty-five minutes to 9. It takes him 10 minutes.

Draw the two times they arrive at school.

Molly

 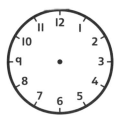

Kasim

Who arrives the earliest? _____

5 Football practice takes 15 minutes.

It starts some time between 4 o'clock and quarter to 5.

What time might football practice finish?

CHALLENGE

Can you think of more than one answer?

Reflect

Explain how you would find what time something ends.

Finding the start time

1 A spelling test ends at half past 2.
The test was 20 minutes long.

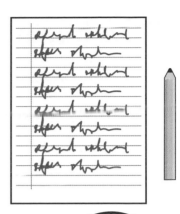

What time did the test start?

end time

time taken

start time

The spelling test started at _____.

2 A cartoon ends at twenty-five minutes
to 9.

It was 15 minutes long.

What time did the cartoon start?

Colour the clocks to show what time
the cartoon started.

end time

time taken

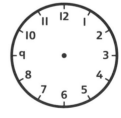

start time

The cartoon started at _____.

3 A bus journey ends at twenty minutes to 6. The journey was 30 minutes long.

What time did the bus journey start?

end time

time taken

start time

The bus journey started at _____.

4 Joe and Anya are reading magazines.

Joe reads for 45 minutes and stops at five minutes to 10.

Anya reads for 35 minutes and stops at ten minutes to 10.

Draw the times they started reading.

Joe

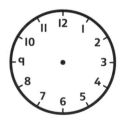

Anya

Who started reading first? _____.

5 A cake takes 35 minutes to bake.

The cake finishes baking some time between quarter to 4 and 4 o'clock.

What time could the cake have started baking?

I wonder if I can think of more than one answer.

Reflect

To find the start time of something, I would

_____

_____

_____

→ Textbook 2C p112

Hours in a day

1 Match up each time with the time 24 hours later.

Wednesday

Wednesday

Tuesday

Thursday

Wednesday

Wednesday

Tuesday

Thursday

2 When is the next flight?

The next aeroplane will

leave on _____

at _____ .

82

3

The bench was painted at twenty minutes past 1 on Thursday afternoon.

The paint takes 24 hours to dry.

It is now half past 2 on Friday afternoon.

Can you sit on the bench?

Time painted on Thursday   Time paint is dry

The paint will be dry at _____

on _____ .

At half past 2 on Friday afternoon, you _____ sit on the bench.

4 Ella has been to the dentist. She is not allowed biscuits for the next 24 hours.

She will be allowed to eat a biscuit on

Monday morning

_____ at _____ .

It is now 9.45 on Tuesday morning.

She _____ eat a biscuit.

CHALLENGE

5 The time is 11 o'clock.

During the next 24 hours, there will be more than seven different o'clock times that have a 1 in them.

Write down as many times with a 1 in as you can.

Is Astrid right?

_____

Reflect

One day is when the hour hand goes once around the clock. For example, from 12 o'clock to 12 o'clock.

You've made a mistake, but that's OK. Let's learn from it!

What is Astrid's mistake?

Use a clock to show your partner what Astrid should have said.

How many hours are there in 2 days? _____

→ Textbook 2C p116

End of unit check

My journal

The answers to these times have been given to you.

Explain how you know whether they are right.

twenty-five
minutes past 6

I know the time is twenty-five
minutes past 6 because

_____

_____

twenty minutes
to 3

I know the time is twenty minutes
to 3 because

_____

_____

These words
might help you.

hour hand

minute hand

85

Power check

How do you feel about your work in this unit?

Power puzzle

Find your way from the START to the FINISH by moving up, down, left or right.

You must only move to a time that is 20 minutes later than the one you are on!

START 4 o'clock	twenty-five past 4	ten past 5	twenty past 7
twenty past 4	twenty to 5	five past 5	twenty-five to 8
ten past 4	5 o'clock	twenty past 5	quarter to 7
half past 4	ten to 5	forty minutes past 5	half past 6
quarter to 5	quarter past 5	6 o'clock	twenty minutes past 6
five to 5	twenty-five past 6	FINISH 7 o'clock	twenty minutes to 7

Comparing mass

1 Use the words **heavier** and **lighter** to complete these sentences.

The zebra is _____ than the camel.

The tiger is _____ than the lion.

The lion is _____ than the camel.

2 Complete the statement.

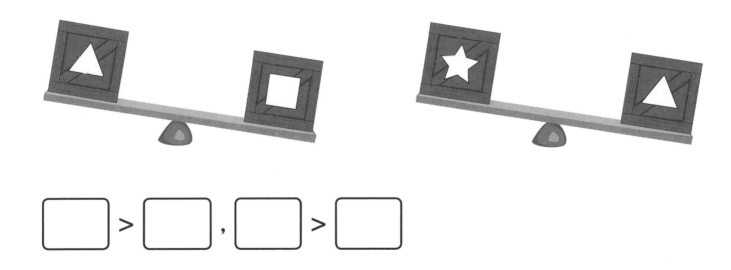

☐ > ☐ , ☐ > ☐

3 **a)** Complete the table.

The △ is twice as heavy as one ▢ .

The ◯ is half as heavy as one ▢ .

The △ is five times as heavy as one ▢ .

Shape	▢	△	◯	△
Mass in cubes	I			

b) Complete the sentences.

The _____ is the heaviest.

The _____ is the lightest.

4 Number the items from lightest (I) to heaviest (3).

CHALLENGE

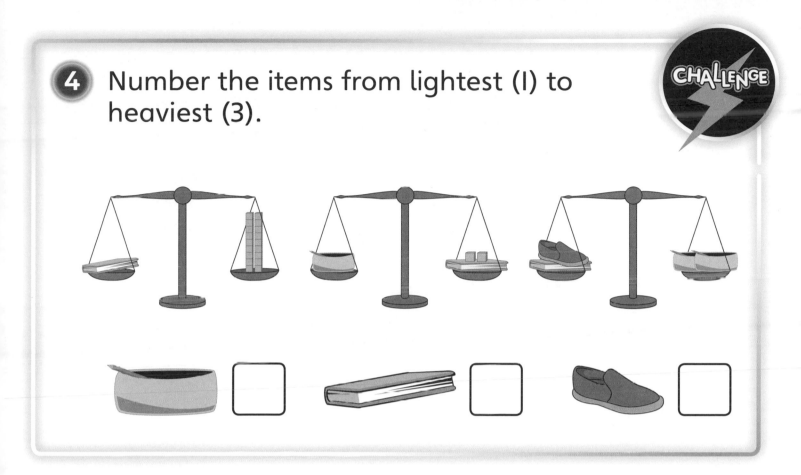

Reflect

Explain what these statements mean.

What can you say about the tin and the box?

→ Textbook 2C p124

Measuring mass in grams

1 Write the mass of each thing in grams.

The mass of the  is ☐ g.

The weighs ☐ g.

2 Show three different ways to make .

Match the to the .

You can only use each once.

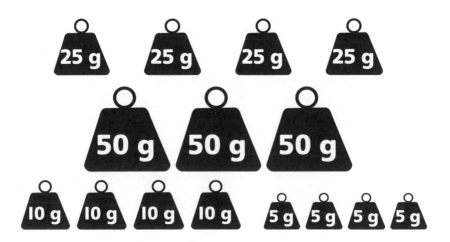

3 **a)** Write the mass of each fruit in grams.

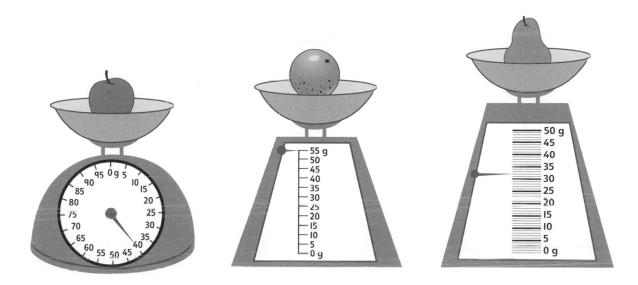

The apple has a mass of ☐ g.

The mass of the orange is ☐ g.

The pear _____ .

b) Draw an arrow on the scale to show the total mass.

4 **a)** Measure the mass of 5 ⬚.

Measure the mass of 10 ⬚.

Mass of 5 ⬚ is ☐ g.

Mass of 10 ⬚ is ☐ g.

CHALLENGE

Can you see a connection?

b) Can you predict the mass of 15 ⬚?

My prediction is ☐ g.

The actual measurement is ☐ g.

Reflect

Rav says, "I have some cheese. How can I find the mass?"

Alia says, "I need 30 grams of cheese. How can I measure it out?"

Explain what is different about what they have to do.

_____

_____

Measuring mass in grams ❷

1 Write the missing numbers on these scales.

a)

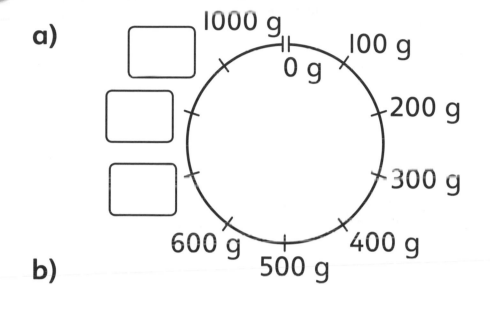

b)

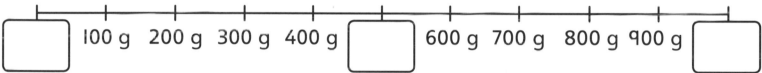

2 Write the mass of each egg to the nearest 100 g.

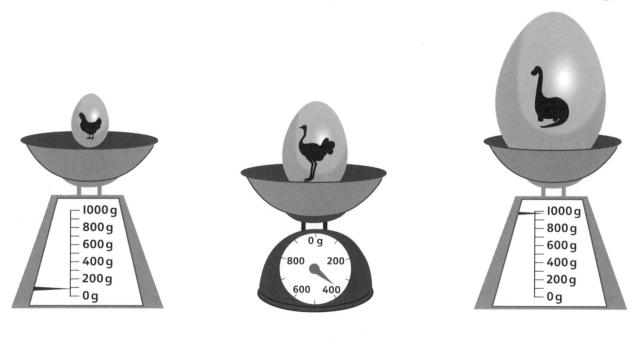

_____   _____   _____

a) Write the mass of each toy in grams.

Mass: Mass: Mass:

☐ g   ☐ g   ☐ g

b) The 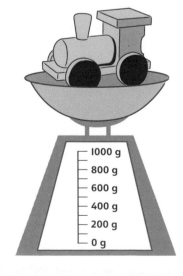 weighs 100 g more than the .

The  weighs 100 g less than the .

The  weighs as much as the and the

 together.

Draw an arrow to show the mass of each toy.

4 Two mystery bags are being balanced.

CHALLENGE

The mass of bag B is between

[ ] g and [ ] g.

Which bag is heavier? _____

I will write a statement for each balance. Bag A > ...

Reflect

Karen says, "Both [guinea pig] have a mass of 600 g to the nearest 100 g."

Steve says, "The black-spotted [guinea pig] is heavier than the golden [guinea pig]."

Explain why they are both right.

_____
_____

→ Textbook 2C p132

Measuring mass in kilograms

1 **a)** Write the mass of each animal in kilograms.

Copy and complete the sentences.

 The has a mass of ☐ kg.

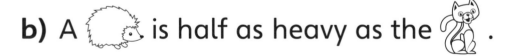 The has a mass of ☐ kg.

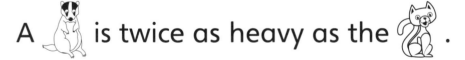 The mass of the is ☐ .

b) A 🦔 is half as heavy as the 🐱 .

A 🦡 is twice as heavy as the 🐱 .

A 🦊 is five times as heavy as the 🦔 .

Use <, > or = to complete these statements.

96

2 **a)** Draw arrows to show the mass of each parcel.

b) Draw arrows to show the total mass on each scale.

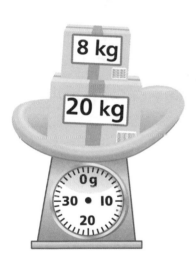 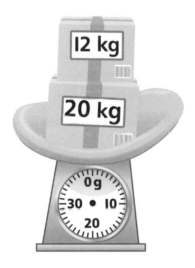 

3 Circle a sensible estimate for the mass of each item.

2 g / 200 g / 2 kg   20 g / 20 kg   200 g / 20 kg

4 Put the suitcases in order of mass.

CHALLENGE

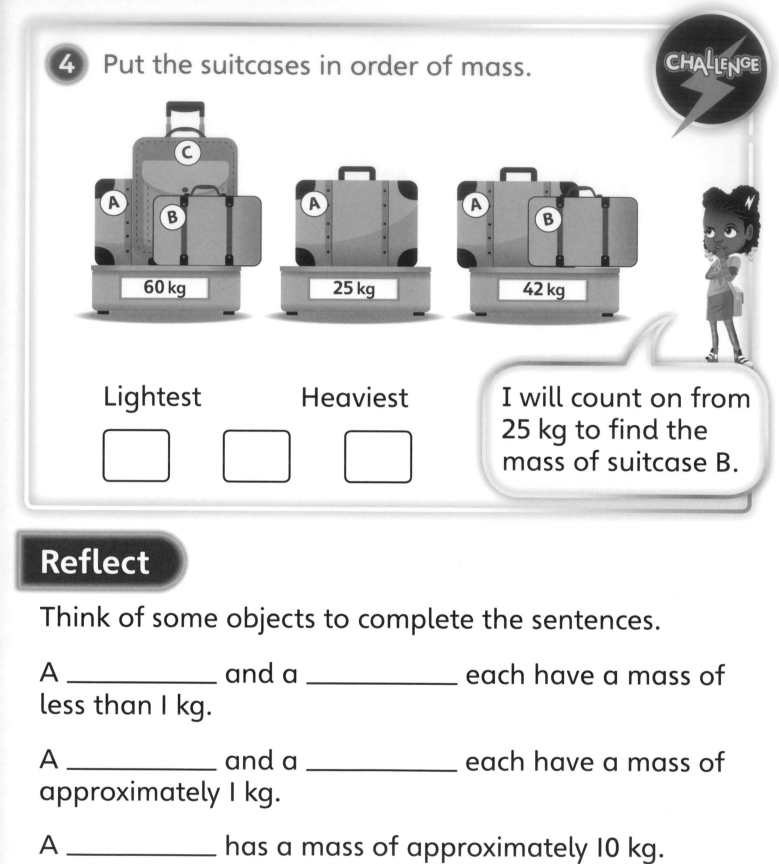

60 kg

25 kg

42 kg

Lightest   Heaviest

I will count on from 25 kg to find the mass of suitcase B.

Reflect

Think of some objects to complete the sentences.

A _____ and a _____ each have a mass of less than I kg.

A _____ and a _____ each have a mass of approximately I kg.

A _____ has a mass of approximately I0 kg.

Comparing volume

1 Complete the sentences using **less** or **more**.

 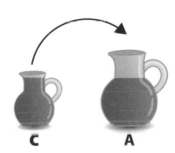

B holds _____ than A.

A holds _____ than C.

C holds _____ than B.

2

 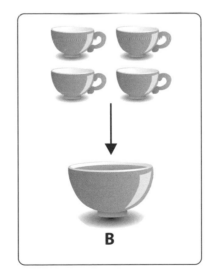 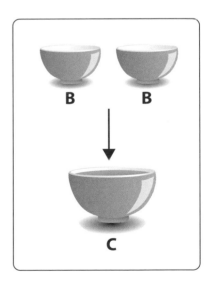

Put the bowls in order of capacity from least to most.

3 Complete the table.

Container	Capacity
	⬜ glasses
	⬜ glasses
	⬜ glasses

4

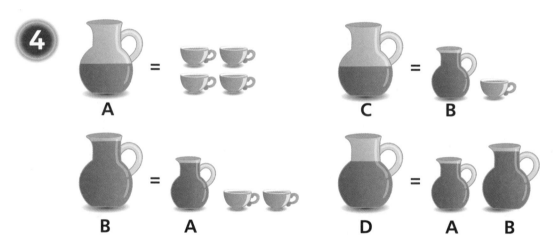

A = (cups)   C = B

B = A   D = A B

Match each 🏺 to the correct bubble.

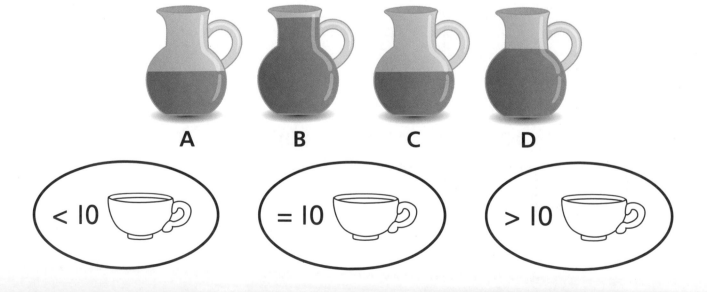

A   B   C   D

< 10   = 10   > 10

5 Milo puts 3 into a  .

Meg puts twice as much into her  .

There are **20**  in a packet.

How much rice is left in the packet?

There are [ ] left

in the packet.

I will cross out the Milo and Meg used.

CHALLENGE

Reflect

How can you tell which has the most rice?

Explain two different ways.

→ Textbook 2C p140

Measuring volume in millilitres ❶

❶ Write the volume of water in each jug.

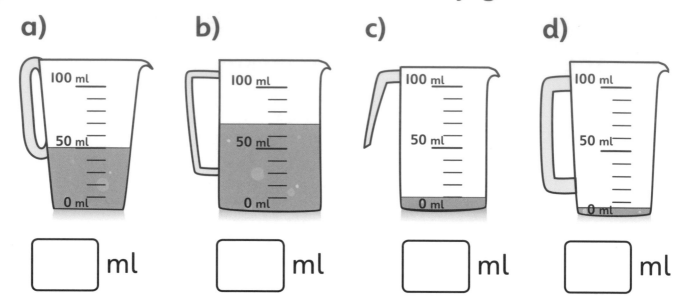

a) [ ] ml   b) [ ] ml   c) [ ] ml   d) [ ] ml

❷ Draw the level of water for each jug.

Remember, a teaspoon holds 5 ml.

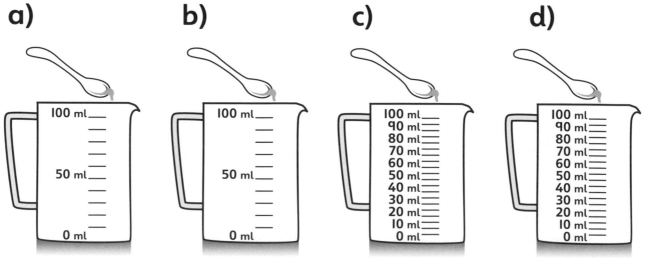

a)   b)   c)   d)

Show 20 ml. Show 90 ml.

3 Tariq used teaspoons to put water in these jugs.

How many teaspoons did he use for each?

a)

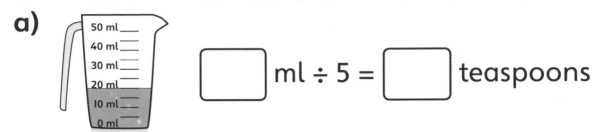

$$\boxed{} \text{ ml} \div 5 = \boxed{} \text{ teaspoons}$$

b)

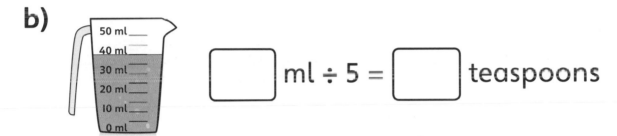

$$\boxed{} \text{ ml} \div 5 = \boxed{} \text{ teaspoons}$$

4 **a)** How much is in the glass?

$$\boxed{} \text{ ml}$$

b) Draw the level to show the volume left in this jug.

103

5 Anya pours a ☕ full of water into a jug.

Then she adds a 🥛 full of water.

Next she fills a ☕ from the jug.

CHALLENGE

What is the capacity of each container?

The ☕ holds [ ] ml.

The 🥛 holds [ ] ml.

The ☕ holds [ ] ml.

Work out how much was in the jug before Anya filled the ☕.

Reflect

How could you measure 20 ml exactly?

Explain two different ways.

- _____
- _____
- _____

Measuring volume in millilitres ❷

1 Write the missing numbers on each scale.

a)

b)

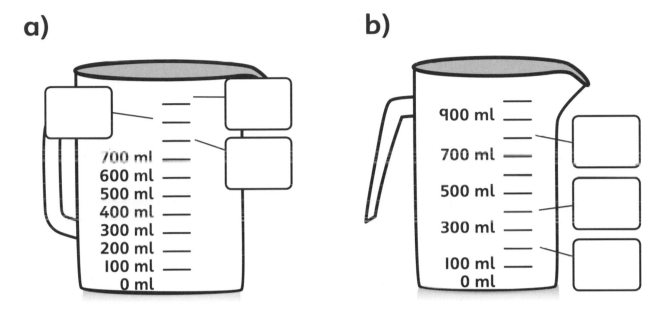

2 Write the volume of water in each jug in millilitres.

a)

b)

c)

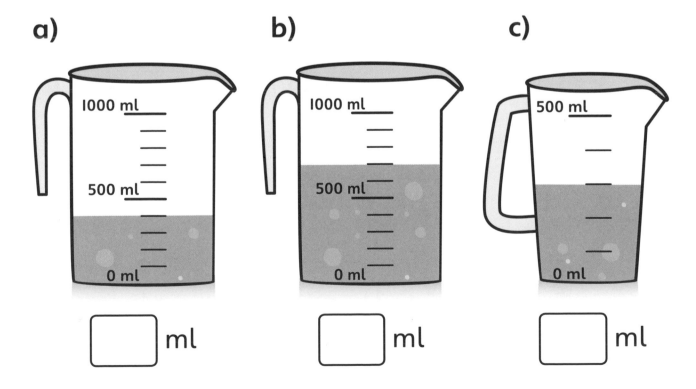

[ ] ml   [ ] ml   [ ] ml

3 Complete the sentences.

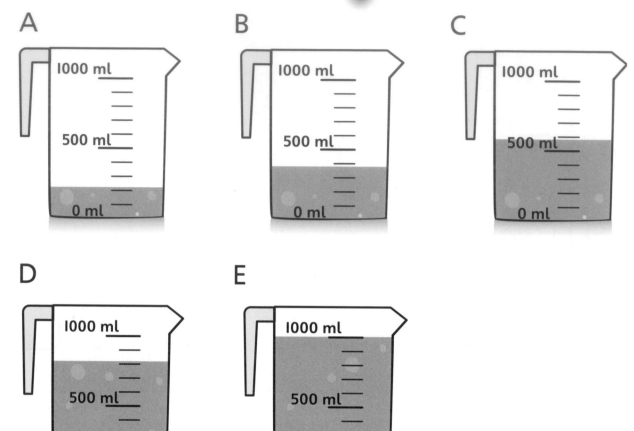

a) Ella needs more than 600 ml but less than 900 ml.

   She could use jug [ ].

b) Kasim needs more than 300 ml but less than 700 ml.

   He could use jug [ ] or jug [ ].

4

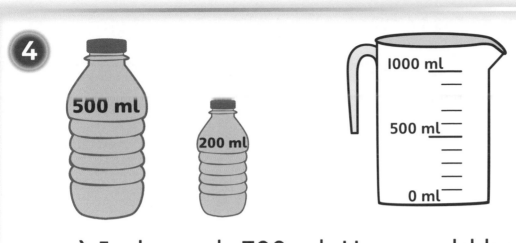

a) Jack needs 700 ml. How could he measure it accurately using the bottles?

I will work out how much more 700 ml is than 500 ml.

b) Kat needs 800 ml. How could she measure exactly 800 ml using the bottles?

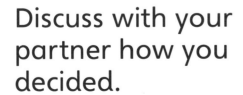

Reflect

Match the capacity to the container.

Discuss with your partner how you decided.

   700 ml

250 ml   700 ml   110 ml

→ Textbook 2C p148

Measuring volume in litres

1

Write the number of litres shown in total.

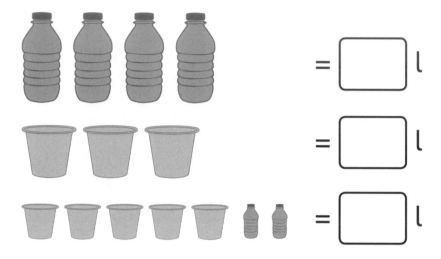

= ☐ l

= ☐ l

= ☐ l

2 **a)** These 🛢 are full of water.

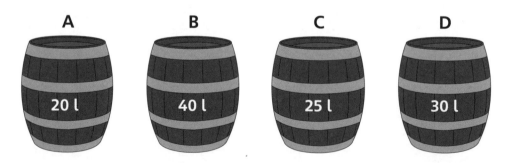

Bill pours 10 l out of each of the four 🛢.

Complete the table.

Barrel	Volume left
A	20 − 10 = 10 l
B	
C	
D	

b) Complete the sentences.

[ ] now has half as much as D.

[ ] now has half as much as B.

B now has [ ] times as much as A.

3 Circle a sensible estimate for each volume.

5 l / 500 l

250 ml / 25 l

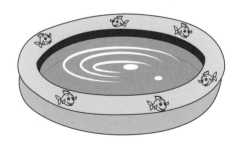

100 ml / 100 l

CHALLENGE

4 Ollie has two buckets.

7 l   4 l

a) Explain how he can measure exactly 3 litres.

b) Explain how he can measure exactly 1 litre.

If I filled the 4 l bucket twice, how much water would I use?

Reflect

Write 3 things you have learned in this unit about how to measure volume.

Use 'ml' and 'l'.

Measuring temperature using a thermometer

1 Write the temperature shown on each 🌡.

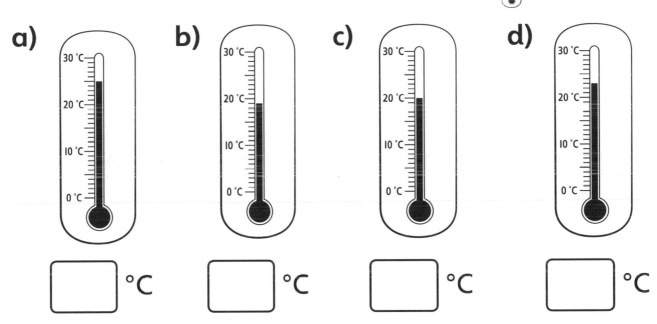

a)　　　　　　b)　　　　　　c)　　　　　　d)

☐ °C　　　☐ °C　　　☐ °C　　　☐ °C

2 Put these temperatures in order, from coolest to warmest.

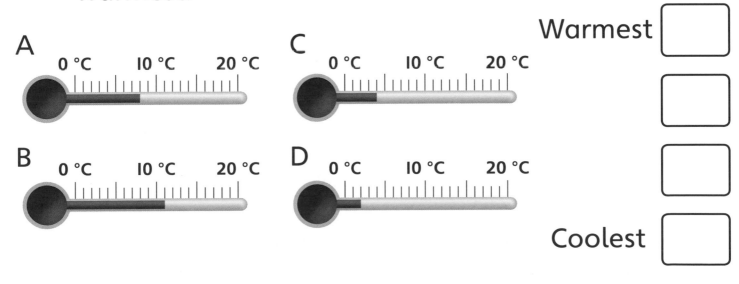

Warmest ☐

☐

☐

Coolest ☐

3 Draw the temperature on the 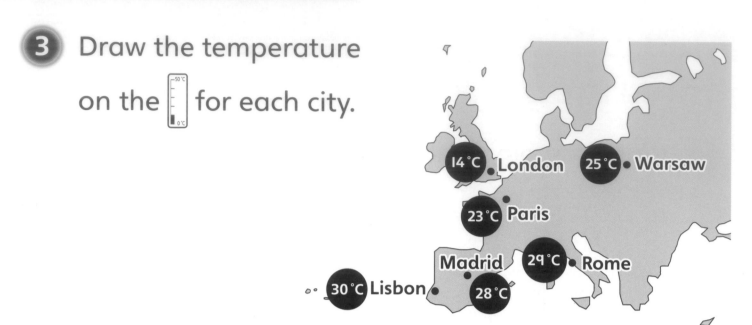 for each city.

Paris

0 °C   10 °C   20 °C   30 °C

Warsaw

0 °C   10 °C   20 °C   30 °C

London

0 °C   10 °C   20 °C   30 °C

Madrid

0 °C   10 °C   20 °C   30 °C

Lisbon

0 °C   10 °C   20 °C   30 °C

Rome

0 °C   10 °C   20 °C   30 °C

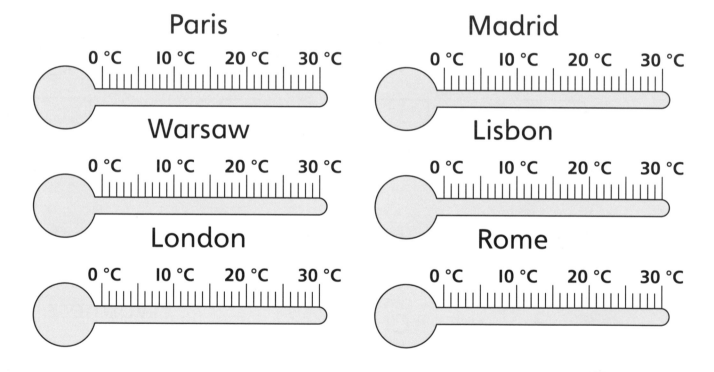

4 Use the map to complete these sentences.

Madrid is ☐ degrees warmer than Paris.

Warsaw is 5 degrees cooler than _____ .

_____ is 2 degrees warmer than _____ .

5 Write two sentences of your own about the map.

CHALLENGE

_____ is _____

than _____ .

> I will start by choosing two cities.

_____ is _____

than _____ .

Reflect

Estimate the temperature in this picture.

Explain your answer.

_____

_____

_____

→ Textbook 2C p156

Reading thermometers

1 Show 20 degrees on each .

a)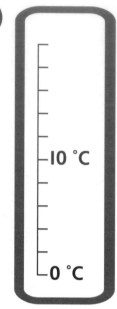

10 °C

0 °C

b)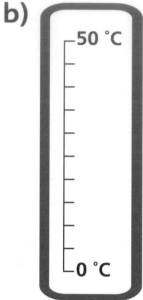

50 °C

0 °C

c)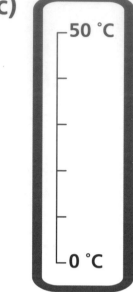

50 °C

0 °C

2 Tick the  that does **not** show 10 degrees.

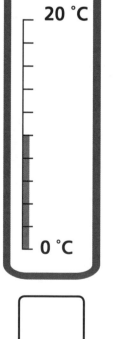

20 °C

0 °C

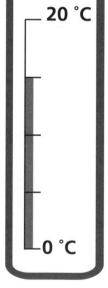

20 °C

0 °C

20 °C

0 °C

3 Tick the 🌡 that shows the hotter temperature.

a) 0°C   10°C

0°C   20°C

b) 0°C   50°C
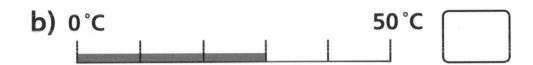

0°C   50°C
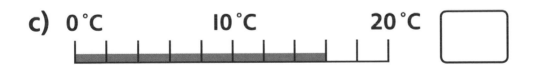

c) 0°C   10°C   20°C

0°C   50°C

d) 0°C   10°C   20°C
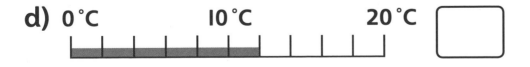

0°C   50°C

4 Draw lines to match each picture to a sensible estimate.

 4 °C

 10 °C

 30 °C

 55 °C

 90 °C

Which picture looks coldest?

Reflect

Explain how you read the different scales on the thermometers that you have used in this unit.

End of unit check

My journal

Milo balances these ☐.

Work out the mass of each ☐.

- First I _____.
- Then I _____.
- Next I _____.

A = ☐ kg   B = ☐ kg   C = ☐ kg

These words might help you.

mass   **kilogram**

divide   **compared**

multiply

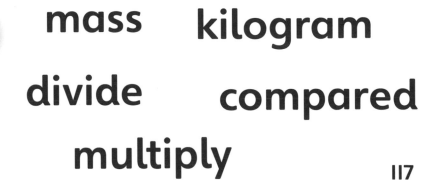

Power check

How do you feel about your work in this unit?

Power puzzle

Weigh an empty .

Measure 100 ml of water into the jug and weigh again.

Repeat for 200 ml and 300 ml.

Write your results in the table.

Volume of water	0 ml	100 ml	200 ml	300 ml
Mass in grams				

I notice that _____

_____

118

My Power Points

Colour in the ☆ to show what you have learned.

Colour in the ☺ if you feel happy about what you have learned.

Unit 11

I can ...

☆ ☺ Use words like **forwards**, **backwards**, **left** and **right** to describe movement

☆ ☺ Describe turns using the words **clockwise** and **anticlockwise**

☆ ☺ Make and describe patterns with shapes that involve turning

Unit 12

I can ...

☆ ☺ Compare different ways to solve problems and work out the best way

☆ ☺ Use number bonds to count on and back from any 2-digit number

☆ ☺ Use a 100 square to quickly add and subtract from any 2-digit number

☆ ☺ Solve missing number problems

☆ ☺ Understand when to use mental methods to add and subtract

☆ ☺ Solve problems using addition, subtraction, multiplication and division

Unit 13

I can ...

☆ ☺ Tell the time to the hour and the half hour

☆ ☺ Tell the time to the quarter hour

☆ ☺ Tell the time to 5 minutes

☆ ☺ Work out how long something takes

☆ ☺ Work out the start and end times

Unit 14

I can ...

☆ ☺ Use balance scales to compare the mass of objects

☆ ☺ Measure mass in grams

☆ ☺ Measure mass in kilograms

☆ ☺ Use containers to compare volume

☆ ☺ Measure volume in millilitres

☆ ☺ Measure volume in litres

☆ ☺ Use and read a thermometer